DAVID
and GOLIATH

by
Barbara Shook Hazen

illustrated by
Robert J. Lee

A GOLDEN BOOK • NEW YORK
Western Publishing Company, Inc.
Racine, Wisconsin 53404

Once, long ago, there lived a great giant named Goliath.
Goliath of Gath was what he was sometimes called, for Gath
was the name of the town where he was born.

Goliath of Gath was the biggest giant that ever lived. His arms were as strong as iron bands, and he was almost as tall as a tree.

He wore a helmet of gleaming brass upon his head and a coat of heavy mail upon his body. The head of his spear weighed over fifteen pounds.

Wherever Goliath went, someone always went before him, carrying Goliath's shield.

The Philistines, who did not believe in God, had set up a camp, high on a mountaintop.

There were many great warriors in the Philistine camp, but the greatest of all was their champion, Goliath of Gath.

Down in the valley, the Israelites had set up their camp. The Israelites did believe in God, and they were willing to defend their belief, even though the Philistine warriors were much bigger and stronger.

But, alas, the Israelites had no champion. And when, every morning and every evening for forty long days, the giant came out and called, "Why don't you send someone to fight me?" there was no one to send. There was no one big enough or strong enough to fight Goliath.

Now, in a town called Bethlehem, there lived a man named Jesse, who had eight sons. The three eldest sons, Eliab, Abinadab, and Shammah, had gone to the camp of the Israelites to help in the fight against the Philistines.

The youngest son, David, stayed at home. His job was to feed his father's sheep in Bethlehem.

One day Jesse said to David, "Take this corn and these ten loaves of bread to your brothers, and take these ten cheeses to the captain of their army. See how your brothers are, and bring me news of the battle."

David got up early the next morning. He left the sheep
with a keeper. He took the corn, the ten loaves of bread, and
the ten cheeses and went to the Israelite camp, as his father,
Jesse, had asked him to do.

When he got there, a battle between the two armies was about to begin.

Quickly David ran to where the warriors were lined up, ready for battle. He saw his brothers and greeted them.

Just then the giant, Goliath, came out again.

"Choose a man to fight me!" he shouted. "If he fights with me and kills me, we will be your servants. But if I kill him, then you will be our servants."

The Israelite warriors were afraid, for they had no champion to fight Goliath for them. "Just look at him!" they cried. "Look at the strength and the size of him!"

David saw how all the men of Israel fled when they saw Goliath. Then David asked, "What shall be done for the man who kills this Philistine?"

The warriors answered, "The man who kills Goliath will be given great riches by Saul, the king of the Israelites."

David's oldest brother, Eliab, was angry at David's question. "Why did you come here?" he asked David. "Are the sheep alone in the wilderness? You are being naughty. You came here just to watch the battle." He glared at David.

Abinadab and Shammah were angry at David, too.

David paid no attention to his brothers. He kept on asking questions about the giant, Goliath.

At last King Saul heard about David. "Bring the boy to me," said the king.

David said to Saul, "Once, when I kept my father's sheep, there came a lion and a bear. They took a lamb from the flock I was tending.

"I went after the lion," said David. "I struck him and took the lamb out of his mouth. And when he rose up against me, I seized him and hit him again and killed him.

"I did the same thing with the bear—and so will I do with this Philistine, this giant, Goliath of Gath, for he has defied the armies of God," said David to King Saul. "The Lord delivered me from the paw of the lion and from the paw of the bear. He will deliver me from the Philistine."

Saul said to David, "Go, and the Lord be with you."

Saul put his own kingly armor on David. He put his own brass helmet on David's head. He put his own coat of mail on David's back. Then Saul gave David his own sword.

But David said, "I cannot go to battle wearing these. I am not used to them."

So David took off Saul's kingly armor and picked up his own shepherd's staff. He carefully chose five smooth stones from the brook and put them in his shepherd's bag.

Then he took his sling in his hand and went to face the mighty Goliath.

When Goliath saw that his enemy was only a boy, he laughed scornfully. "Am I a dog," Goliath asked, "that you think you can beat me with a stick?"

David said, "You fight with a sword and a spear and a shield. I fight in the name of the Lord. God will deliver you into my hand this day!"

Hearing this, Goliath went to meet David—and David went to meet the giant.

David took a stone out of his shepherd's bag. Whirling the stone in his sling, he hurled the stone at Goliath and hit him in the middle of his forehead.

The great giant fell dead, facedown on the ground. The frightened Philistine army turned and fled in panic.

So, long ago, the shepherd boy David killed the great Goliath—with a sling and a stone and a mighty belief in God.